3 Beloved Tales

Rapunzel

stories around the World

by Cari Meister

What is a fairy tale?

Once upon a time, before the age of books, people gathered to tell stories. They told tales of fairies and magic, princes and witches. Ideas of love, jealousy, kindness and luck filled the stories. Some provided lessons. Others simply entertained. Most did both! These fairy tales passed from neighbour to neighbour, village to village, land to land. As the stories spun across seas and over mountains, details changed to fit each culture. A poisoned slipper became a poisoned ring. A king became a sultan. A wolf became a tiger.

Over time, fairy tales were collected and written down. Around the world today, people of all ages love to read or listen to these timeless stories. For many years to come, fairy tales will continue to live happily ever after in our imaginations.

Rapunzel

illustrated by
Valentina Belloni

A German fairy tale

Once upon a time, there lived a man and a woman who desperately wanted to have a baby. Year after year they waited. No baby came.

The couple lived next to a sorceress who had a magnificent garden. One day the woman noticed a bed of rapunzel. It looked so delicious. She longed for it more than anything.

"If I don't have that rapunzel," the woman told her husband, "I will die."

So the man climbed over the garden wall and stole a handful for her. Oh, how fresh and crunchy it tasted! His wife was content that night.

The next day, she asked for more.

Again the husband climbed over the wall. This time the sorceress was waiting.

"How dare you steal from me!" she yelled. "You will pay for this!"

"Be merciful," the man begged. "My wife saw your rapunzel and was overcome with longing for it."

"Very well," the sorceress said. "Take the rapunzel, but under one condition: I will take your first child in return."

The man, not knowing what else to do, agreed.

In time the woman gave birth to a baby girl. True to the agreement, the sorceress took the child. She named her Rapunzel and locked her in a tall tower near the forest. The tower had only a small window at the top.

Rapunzel grew into a beautiful woman with long golden hair. Whenever the sorceress wanted to see her, she would call, "Rapunzel, Rapunzel, let down your hair!"

Rapunzel would lean out of the window and let her hair fall to the ground. Up the sorceress would climb.

One day a prince was riding through the forest. He heard Rapunzel singing. The prince wanted to see her, but there was no way into the tower.

The next day the prince returned. He hid behind a tree and watched as the sorceress called out and climbed up Rapunzel's hair.

After the sorceress left, the prince tried. "Rapunzel, Rapunzel, let down your hair!" he said. The golden hair appeared, and up the prince climbed.

The prince instantly fell in love. When he asked Rapunzel to marry him, she agreed. But she had no way out of the tower.

"Each time you visit," she said, "bring some silk. I will tie it together to make a rope."

So, little by little, the silk rope grew.

Soon the sorceress found out about the prince. Furious, she cut off Rapunzel's hair and cast her deep into the woods. Then she waited in the tower for the prince.

When the prince called, "Rapunzel, Rapunzel, let down your hair," the sorceress let down Rapunzel's hair. When the prince reached the window, the sorceress cackled.

"You will never find Rapunzel!" she squawked. "She's gone forever!"

Full of sadness the prince leaped, landing on a thorn bush that poked at his eyes. The prince wandered the woods, blind and heartbroken, for many years.

Then one day he heard singing. Rapunzel! Upon seeing her prince, Rapunzel cried. Her tears fell into his eyes, and his sight returned. Rapunzel and the prince found their way back to his kingdom, where they lived happily ever after.

Clotilde

illustrated by
Eva Montanari

A Filipino fairy tale

Long ago in a distant land, there lived a king called
Ludovico. Ludovico was friends with a magician who was
deeply in love with Ludovico's daughter, Clotilde. But
beautiful Clotilde was not interested in the old magician.

Spurned, the magician turned
bitter. Before he died he locked
Clotilde, three magical horses and two
magical necklaces in a tall tower.

Ludovico was deeply saddened. He offered money, his daughter's hand in marriage and the kingdom itself to any man who could set his daughter free.

Hundreds of men – princes and peasants – tried. All failed. The tower was simply too tall.

At last a man called Juan arrived. Both of Juan's brothers had tried to climb the tower and failed. They told Juan not to try. His parents also told him not to try. "You will shame us if you fail," they said.

But Juan was strong-willed. He was also kind-hearted, clever and very handsome.

Juan gathered nails, a long rope
and a hammer. He drove the nails
into the tower. Then he tied the
rope to the nails. After several
days he made a rope ladder
that reached all the way to
Clotilde's window.

When Clotilde and Juan saw each other, they fell instantly in love.

"Please, take one of my necklaces as a sign of my love," she said.

But before Juan could thank her, his rope ladder began to give way.

Juan's jealous brother had pulled out all the nails!

"I shall fall to my death!" Juan cried.

Clotilde quickly called to one of the magical horses. She told Juan to jump on, and he did.

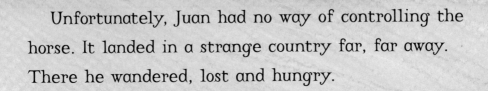

Unfortunately, Juan had no way of controlling the
horse. It landed in a strange country far, far away.
There he wandered, lost and hungry.

Many years passed before Juan found his way home. He wanted to see Clotilde, but he guessed that she was already happily married to someone else.

Heartbroken, Juan found work with a kind old man called Telesforo.

Meanwhile, King Ludovico had made another proclamation: Whoever could match his daughter's necklace could marry her. Many tried to copy Clotilde's necklace, but all failed.

News of the proclamation reached Juan. He wrapped up the necklace Clotilde had given him and asked Telesforo to take it to the palace.

When Clotilde saw the necklace, she gasped. She knew it was the one she had given Juan. Telesforo told her that Juan was alive. Clotilde was filled with joy.

Shortly thereafter Clotilde and Juan were married. King Juan and Queen Clotilde lived to old age, ruling their lands in peace and happiness.

Petrosinella

An Italian fairy tale *illustrated by Colleen Madden*

Once upon a time in Italy, there lived a woman called Pascadozzia. One day Pascadozzia saw a beautiful parsley plant in the garden of her neighbour, the ogress. Oh, how she longed for the parsley! So great was her longing that she crept into the garden and stole some. This went on for days until, one day, the ogress caught her.

"Thief!" exclaimed the ogress. "Now you must pay."

Pascadozzia tried to make excuses. But the ogress shrugged her shoulders and said, "Words are but wind. You must die OR give me your first child."

Poor Pascadozzia agreed to give the ogress her child.

Some months later Pascadozzia gave birth to a baby girl. She called her Parsley, because she was born with a sprig of parsley on her chest. When Parsley was seven years old, the ogress snatched her away. She locked the girl in a tall tower. Whenever the ogress wanted to see Parsley, she climbed up the girl's long hair.

Many years later a prince appeared. He saw
Parsley's hair hanging from the tower window.
He called out. When their eyes met, the prince
and Parsley fell instantly in love.

The prince wanted to climb up.
But the visit had to be kept secret.
So Parsley secretly gave the ogress
poppy juice. The juice made the
ogress fall into a deep sleep.

The next morning, as the prince climbed down Parsley's hair, a friend of the ogress saw him.

She told the ogress, who replied, "Thank you. But do not fear. It's impossible for Parsley to escape. I have laid a spell upon her. Unless she's holding the three gallnuts that are hidden above the kitchen rafters, the spell cannot be broken."

Luckily Parsley overheard
the ogress. That night, when
the prince came, she told him
to climb the rafters and get
the gallnuts. Then, holding the
gallnuts in her hand, she and
the prince climbed down a rope
ladder and escaped.

The ogress' friend saw them. She called
out and woke the ogress, who quickly chased
after Parsley and the prince.

Parsley, knowing the gallnuts were magical, threw one
at the ground. It turned into a Corsican bulldog! The beast
chomped its jaws and leapt at the ogress. But the cunning
ogress pulled out a piece of bread and gave it to the dog,
which made the dog's anger disappear.

Parsley threw the second gallnut. It turned into a lion! The beast shook its mane and opened its jaws wide.

But the ogress stripped off the skin of a donkey that was grazing near by. Wearing the skin, she charged the lion. The lion, thinking the ogress was an angry donkey, became frightened and ran away.

Parsley looked into her hand. She had one gallnut left. She threw it, and it turned into a wolf! Seeing the ogress in the donkey skin, the hungry wolf pounced. In a blink, it ate her.

At last Parsley and the prince were free of the ogress. They married and lived happily ever after.

Glossary

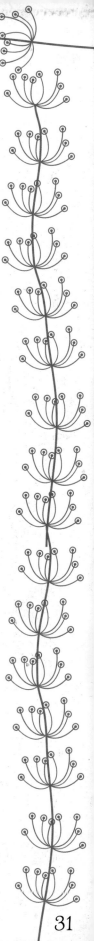

Corsican bulldog bulldog with large jaws that comes from the Italian island of Corsica

culture people's way of life, ideas, art, customs and traditions

gallnut abnormal growth of plant tissue (often found on oak trees) that looks like a nut

ogress female monster or giant that eats people; the male version is called an ogre

proclamation official announcement

rapunzel type of flowering plant that has a white, edible root; also known as rampion

sorceress woman with magical powers

spurn turn away or reject

Comprehension questions

Look at the illustrations for *Rapunzel*. What details show you that the story takes place in Germany?

How do Juan's actions contribute to the sequence of events in *Clotilde*?

What does the ogress in *Petrosinella* mean when she says, "Words are but wind?"

Writing prompts

1) Write your own version of *Petrosinella* set in modern times. What could you use instead of gallnuts? What creatures could you write about instead of a Corsican bulldog, a lion and a wolf?

2) Write a "reader's theatre" script for one of the stories in this book.

Read more

Grimm's Fairy Tales (Usborne Illustrated), retold by Ruth Brocklehurst & Gillian Doherty (Usborne Publishing Ltd, 2011)

Ratpunzel (Animal Fairy Tales), Charlotte Guillain (Raintree, 2013)

The Unhappy Stonecutter: A Japanese Folk Tale (Folk Tales from Around the World), Charlotte Guillain (Raintree, 2014)

Raintree is an imprint of Capstone Global Library Limited, a company incorporated in England and Wales having its registered office at 264 Banbury Road, Oxford, OX2 7DY – Registered company number: 6695582

www.raintree.co.uk
myorders@raintree.co.uk

Text ©Capstone Global Library Limited 2016
The moral rights of the proprietor have been asserted.

Editor: Jill Kalz
Designer: Ashlee Suker
Art Director: Nathan Gassman
Production Specialist: Katy LaVigne
The illustrations in this book were created digitally.

Printed in China
ISBN 978 1 4747 2418 0
20 19 18 17 16
10 9 8 7 6 5 4 3 2 1

Website

www.booktrust.org.uk/books/children/illustrators/illustrations-in-search-of-a-story/

Make your own book with Chris Riddell!

British Library Cataloguing in Publication Data
A full catalogue record for this book is available from the British Library.

Acknowledgements
Thanks to our advisers for their expertise and advice:

Maria Tatar, PhD, Chair, Program in Folklore & Mythology
John L. Loeb Professor of Germanic Languages & Literatures and Folklore & Mythology, Harvard University

Terry Flaherty, PhD, Professor of English
Minnesota State University, Mankato

Look out for all the books in this series:

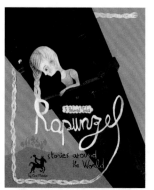
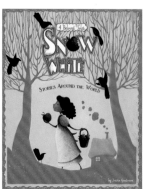